SRA
OPEN COURT READING

Little Hare

SRA

A Division of The McGraw·Hill Companies

Columbus, Ohio

www.sra4kids.com

SRA/McGraw-Hill

A Division of The **McGraw·Hill** Companies

Send all inquiries to:
SRA/McGraw-Hill
8787 Orion Place
Columbus, OH 43240-4027

ISBN 0-07-569994-X
    3 4 5 6 7 8 9 DBH 05 04 03 02

Old Hare's Plan

Lion had a fierce appetite. No matter how much he ate, he was unsatisfied. Some told that Lion could eat fifty elephants and twenty giraffes and ten zebras at once—and then enjoy more.

Each day Lion raided an animal village and ate everything in sight. The animals were fearful.

Old Hare—the oldest and wisest animal—
called an emergency meeting.

Old Hare cleared his throat, and the crowd fell
silent.

"I have a plan," he began, "that will save our
village and put an end to Lion."

4

A great noise rose from the crowd. Old Hare
called for silence.

"Each day," he continued, "one of us will go to
Lion and offer to be eaten. Then Lion will leave
the rest of us alone."

There were loud hurrays. But the animals were
unwilling to volunteer.

Just then Little Hare piped up. "I will go," she said quietly.

"Three cheers for Little Hare!" cried the animals. "Farewell, farewell, brave Little Hare!" they called out. But really they thought she was foolish.

Little Hare knocked at Lion's den.
"What?" bellowed Lion.
"My name is Little Hare," said Little Hare. "I am
here to be your next meal. More creatures will
follow me each day. You will never be hungry
again."

"Ho, ho!" roared Lion, flashing his big, shiny teeth. "You will never satisfy my hunger. I will be unsatisfied."

"Almost there!" Little Hare sang out. "Just a little bit farther!" And still they walked, and still there was no big lion.

"I've had it!" cried Lion in disgust. "You have tricked me! There is no big lion. There is just me and you—and I am going to eat YOU right now!"

Just then Little Hare began to hop up and down.

"Look!" she cried. "In the river! I see him!"

Lion raced to the riverbank and stared into the water.

Lion roared, "So you robbed me of my meal! Come out of the water and fight!"

But the big lion stayed put.

"If you won't come out and fight," Lion growled, "I'll come in and get you." Lion bared his teeth and narrowed his eyes. So did the big lion.

With a great roar, Lion jumped into the river. Little Hare stood by and watched from behind the tall grass. Then she quickly ran back to the village before Lion came out of the water.

When Little Hare returned to her village, she shared her news with the happy crowd. "Lion will not be able to find his way back to our village. We will never see that lion again."